# Think and Grow Rich

## *Workbook*

*The Consultant and Knowledge Workers Edition of the best selling classic, Think & Grow Rich, by Napoleon Hill*

## Toks K. Oyegunle

Think and Grow Rich Workbook: The Consultant and Knowledge Workers Edition

© 2012 www.TheConsultantsAcademy.com

Think and Grow Rich
By Napoleon Hill
Copyright © 1937, The Ralston Society
Revised by Toks K. Oyegunle, derivative work copyright © 2012 TheConsultantsAcademy.com

Published by:
The Consultants Academy
info@TheConsultantsAcademy.com
www.TheConsultantsAcademy.com

This book contains the opinions and ideas of its author. The strategies outlined may not be suitable for every individual and are not guaranteed or warranted to produce any particular results. It is sold with the understanding that neither the publisher, nor author is engaged in rendering legal, tax, investment, insurance, financial, accounting, or professional advice. The author strongly recommends that if the reader requires any such advice or services, a competent professional should be consulted.

Every effort has been made to make this book as complete and as accurate as possible. However, there may be mistakes, both typographical and in content. Therefore, this text should be used only as a general guide. Furthermore, this book contains information based on the author's research and experience that is current only up to the printing date. Thoughts and opinions may change. No warranty is made with respect to the accuracy or completeness of the information contained herein, and both the author and the publisher specifically disclaim any responsibility for any liability, loss or risk personal or otherwise, which is incurred as a consequence, directly or indirectly, of the use and application of any of the contents of this book.

ISBN: 978-0-9858209-9-2

# Contents

# Author's Preface

Toks K. Oyegunle

To become a professional consultant was my career goal for a long time; I aspired to be the smart consultant companies called on to solve their problems. I chose to specialise in computing at university and had a clear vision of becoming one of the top IT Consultants in the market. I was so keen on this goal that, for the final year dissertation of my BSc degree in Computing, I chose a practical project that gave me the exciting opportunity to be a "real life" consultant helping a small business deal with a real business challenge.

I had to go to the "client site" which was a small chain of 4 pizza take away shops in North London at the time. I met with the owner, an ambitious entrepreneur from Iran with a big vision to create a chain of Pizza outlets. This was fun for me and I helped them develop a Stock & Cash Management system that reduced costs and increased sales at the same time. Shortly after this, the chain introduced franchising and grew to 22 outlets and one main franchisor company that supplied the ingredients and products to all the outlets. I was very impressed with the growth and learned the potential of rapid expansion and financial success for determined entrepreneurs.

I went on to get a Master's degree in Business Systems Analysis & Design from City University in the City of London, as this was the best course in the City that linked Business with IT. Shortly after this I became a Junior Consultant with a niche consultancy that specialized in providing Financial Technology solutions for the Investment Banking sector. It was such an exciting time as we only turned up when there was a problem, fixed it and moved on to the next challenge and client site. Being a serial entrepreneur at heart, I soon left paid employment to set up shop as an Independent Consultant helping many investment banks deal with technology based challenges.

After this I went on to set up a Recruitment Consultancy that supplied technology consultants to major companies; I also set up a Financial Technology Consultancy & Software House that provided consultancy and systems to many banks. I have been privileged to be a consultant to governments advising on IT Policy and also advised non profits on business development and growth strategies.

Nowadays I am regularly called the "Consultants Consultant" as I help many consultants and knowledge workers with their development, growth, and marketing strategies. This was one of the main reasons why I decided to create this workbook.

I have been using *Think & Grow Rich* for more than 20 years and it has made an enormous impact on my life. As a poor kid growing up in the slums in Africa I always had dreams of getting rich as a means of getting out of poverty. Each time I remember my rather humble beginnings I am always grateful for how far I have come. I have found a way to develop myself from abject poverty to considerable success, I guess finding a way to attend some of the best schools in the world like the Harvard Business School and the City University greatly helped.

Looking back, however, I realize that my growth and accelerated success has been mainly due to my ability to read widely and educate myself continuously on the fundamental requirements of success. Yes, poverty may have given me the hunger and desire for success but reading self development books, especially *"Think & Grow Rich"* coupled with a firm commitment to continuous learning definitely gave me the tools and techniques to make success possible.

As part of my desire to give back to humanity, I am fully committed to helping as many people as possible achieve financial success from their knowledge, skills, and experience. This workbook will be extremely helpful to you if you are a consultant or knowledge worker already or if you are aspiring to become one. Consultants are actually paid to "Think and Solve Problems" so why cant they "Think and Grow Rich"? It is interesting that we currently live in the information age, where knowledge and information have become extremely valuable in the right hands of people who know what to do with it.

The sad truth is that most consultants do NOT get rich unfortunately. Consultants mostly get somewhat comfortable, but then they typically fall into the middle class abyss typified by consumer debt and a continuous struggle to make ends meet. There are many reasons for this and this workbook will help you discover how YOU can become rich using the knowledge, skills, and experience you have acquired as a consultant or knowledge worker.

I am keen to learn how you have applied what you learn from this workbook to your life to create wealth. I wish you good luck and may God bless you abundantly.

Toks K. Oyegunle

Founder
The Consultants Academy
Toks@TheConsultantsAcademy.com
www.TheConsultantsAcademy.com

**PS: There is a very important FREE BONUS OFFER from me on page 71 of this workbook. This gift can dramatically boost your success as a Consultant while increasing your profit considerably. It is also the ideal way to continue our relationship beyond this workbook. Please take a minute to act on it.**

# How to Use this Workbook

As a consultant or knowledge worker you are probably used to finding solutions to various client challenges and issues. But, really, who is responsible for solving your challenge of becoming rich? YOU!

This was exactly why the *Think and Grow Rich Workbook for Consultants and Knowledge Workers* has been created— to help consultants and knowledge workers help themselves by creating a personalized solution to their own financial challenges for a change.

For you to get the maximum benefit of these 13 principles of success, you need to do more than just read about them in a passive state. In order to fully experience the level of success that is possible, you need to apply these concepts to your individual circumstances. This workbook will help you to take each of the 13 principles and take successful action by applying them to your life and create a unique personalized strategy that will provide you with a crystal clear path to the riches you deserve. As Napoleon Hill says, "Reduce your plan to writing. The moment you complete this, you will have definitely given concrete form to the intangible desire".

You should start by identifying a quiet, comfortable place where you can think and will not be disturbed. This is a workbook and requires you to review your life in detail and reflect on the best way forward. Read the brief summary of each chapter once or twice to refresh your memory on the contents, while reading the summary, think about what it means in general but consider how it affects you in particular.

Then proceed to answer all the questions immediately, you need to be extremely honest with yourself while doing this. Do not second guess yourself and typically you should go with your first response and follow your gut feeling. Try to answer as many questions as you can at a go and do not review your individual answers until you have finished the entire workbook. This is necessary so you create a frank, realistic and objective overview of your plans of becoming a Rich Consultant.

Please understand there is no right or wrong answer here. This is a personal exercise for you and you alone, although you may want to discuss your findings with a member of your mastermind (preferably if they have completed the workbook too) for some mutual support and realistic feedback. Ultimately your goal with this workbook is one of increased self awareness and crystal clear clarity on what is required for you to become a Rich Consultant!

I suggest you should get a journal to record your thoughts, insights and feelings as you go through this workbook and even after you complete it. You will start to think differently as your understanding of the "Think & Grow Rich" mindset increases and you should record all new ideas, potential strategies and plans as they may be extremely helpful to you moving forward.

Let's get started!

# Preface

## Key Ideas

1. Success doesn't come through formal education.

2. The secret will work for you if you know what you want.

3. *Think and Grow Rich for Consultants and Knowledge Workers* is not only about material wealth.

4. This book won't tell you what the secret it, you have to discover it yourself.

5. You have to be mentally ready for the secret.

6. You already have half of the secret in your mind.

7. Once you start applying it, you might find yourself swept away to success.

8. The book will teach you not only what to do, but how to do it, and how to start.

## Exercises

1.  What is your level of formal education?

    _____

    _____

    _____

2.  How has your formal education helped you be successful? How has it not?

    _____

    _____

    _____

3.  What specialized experience do you have?

    _____

    _____

    _____

4.  How has your specialized experience helped you be successful? How has it not?

    _____

    _____

    _____

5.  In the following space, describe your level of mental readiness to learn the secret to becoming rich:

    _____

    _____

    _____

# Chapter 1 — Introduction

## Key Ideas

1.  Thoughts are things, when mixed with definiteness of purpose, persistence, and a BURNING DESIRE they translate into wealth.

2.  It matters less what you say than what you think.

3.  You have to be ready and be determined to persevere until you attain what you want.

4.  Opportunity often comes disguised as misfortune and defeat.

5.  One of the most common causes of failure is quitting as soon as you experience temporary defeat.

6.  Even if you have quit before, you can learn from the experience and become a "sticker" instead of a quitter in the future.

7.  Most successful people say that their greatest success came one step beyond an apparent failure or defeat.

8.  Once you get it, the wealth starts flowing at a surprising rate.

9.  After the Great Depression, things changed back very, very slowly. It was almost imperceptible.

10. You already know the rules that make things seem impossible. This book highlights the rules that those who succeeded followed.

11. Success comes to those who are success conscious. Failure comes to those who are failure conscious.

12. Most people can't believe something that they haven't experienced already or that they don't understand.

13. The universal power is going to turn positive thoughts into positive things and negative thoughts into negative things. It is in this way that you are the Master of your Fate and the Captain of your Soul.

14. The thoughts you think the most—either positive or negative—become magnets to experiences that reinforce it.

15. In order to get rich, you have to develop an intense, burning desire to have money and that will cause you to create a definite plan for getting it.

## Exercises

1.  Describe a time when you experienced misfortune or defeat and it became an opportunity.

    _____

    _____

    _____

2.  What is the current challenge you are facing?

    _____

    _____

    _____

3.  Can you see an opportunity in it?

    _____

    _____

    _____

4.  Would you say that you have a tendency to be more of a positive thinker or a negative thinker? How has that manifested into your life?

    _____

    _____

    _____

5.  Set an alarm to go off every three hours and do this four times. When it goes off, make a note of what you were thinking at the time. Write those thoughts down here:

    One: _____

    _____

    _____

    Two: _____

    _____

    _____

Three: _____

_____

_____

Four: _____

_____

_____

6. What was the nature of your thoughts? Were they "success conscious" or "poverty conscious?"

_____

_____

_____

7. Tomorrow, do the same exercise, and if the thoughts are negative or of a poverty consciousness, make an effort to think of something positive or successful. Doing this regularly will help to train your brain to think positively.

_____

_____

_____

# Chapter 2 — Desire: The Starting Point of All Achievement

## Key Ideas

1.  Success doesn't come as a "big break." It happens long in your mind before you ever get your break.

2.  You have to leave yourself no opportunity for retreat. Don't "try" and see if you'll succeed. Make your mind up with a definite purpose that you will.

3.  Wishing will not bring riches. But desiring riches with a state of mind that becomes an obsession, then planning definite ways and means to acquire riches, and backing those plans with action will make you rich.

4.  The object is to want money, and to become so determined to have it that you actually CONVINCE yourself you will have it.

5.  "Money consciousness" means that the mind has become so thoroughly saturated with the DESIRE for money, that you can see yourself already in possession of it.

6.  Every great leader that ever existed was a dreamer.

7.  Every failure carries within it the seed of an even greater success.

8.  Everyone who has succeeded first had challenges and setbacks and failure. It was at the time of crisis that they discovered their "other selves," which led them to their greatest success.

9.  Most people never learn how to transmute (change) their strongest negative emotion into something positive.

10. There is a difference between WISHING for a thing and being READY to receive it. No one is ready for a thing, until he believes he can acquire it. The state of mind must be BELIEF, not mere hope or wish. Open-mindedness is essential for belief. Closed minds do not inspire faith, courage, and belief.

## Exercises

1. How can you completely commit to your success? What can you do to eliminate all opportunity for retreat?

   _____

   _____

   _____

2. In the following space, write down your BURNING PASSIONATE DESIRE for riches. Don't just write a sentence, but feel it with all the passion in your heart.

   _____

   _____

   _____

3. Describe what it will be like when you are already in possession of your desire.

   _____

   _____

   _____

4. Do you truly believe that you can have it? Or, are you just wishing for it?

   _____

   _____

   _____

# Chapter 3 — Faith Visualization of, and Belief in Attainment of Desire

## Key Ideas

1.  Faith is a state of mind that can be created by saying affirmations (or auto-suggestions).

2.  Thoughts that have been mixed with faith, or any of the other positive emotions are the ones that get implanted in the subconscious and are the ones that come true.

3.  The same thing is true of negative thoughts and emotions.

4.  The best way to speed the process of manifestation along is to act as if what you want is already true.

5.  When Napoleon Hill talks about faith, he's not necessarily talking about religious faith. He's talking about believing that your dream will come true.

6.  Taking inventory of mental assets and liabilities, you will discover that your greatest weakness is lack of self-confidence.

7.  There are six steps to achieving a great goal. They are:

8.  **First,** create an IDEA through your IMAGINATION.

9.  **Second,** mix FAITH with your IDEA.

10. **Third,** formulate a PLAN for the transformation of your IDEA into physical and financial reality.

11. **Fourth,** put your plan into action.

12. **Fifth,** apply and follow through on your PLAN with PERSISTENCE, and back it with firm DECISION until it has been fully carried out.

13. **Sixth,** prepare the way for success by having a BURNING DESIRE for success.

14. RICHES begin in the form of THOUGHT! The amount is limited only by the person in whose mind the THOUGHT is put into motion. FAITH removes limitations!

## Exercises

1.  Look at your calendar and plan an "act as if" day. In other words, take one day and act as if you were already wealthy. What would you do? Would you test drive new cars? Attend open house events in an expensive neighborhood? Plan an exotic vacation? In the following space, write down what you will do on your "as if" day.

    _____

    _____

    _____

2.  In this next section, walk through the six steps to achieving a great goal.

    Step One: What is your IDEA? _____

    _____

    Step Two: How much FAITH do you have mixed in with that idea? _____

    _____

    Step Three: What is your PLAN for manifesting that idea? _____

    _____

    Step Four: What is one action that you can take today? _____

    _____

    Step Five: What decisions have you made that will allow you to stay focused and persistent when things get tough? _____

    _____

    Step Six: How can you FEEL your Burning Desire for success every day? _____

    _____

# Chapter 4 — Auto-Suggestion the Medium for Influencing the Subconscious Mind

## Key Ideas

1. Nothing enters the subconscious mind until it goes through the conscious mind. You have control over it, whether you're exercising control or not.

2. The way to train the conscious mind to imprint something into the subconscious mind is to read aloud a written statement of what you want several times a day and to see and feel yourself already in possession of it.

3. Don't get discouraged if you have trouble directing your thoughts and emotions right away. That's the price you have to pay for success. Just keep at it and you'll learn how to do it.

4. Close your eyes and actually SEE yourself in possession of the specific amount of money you want.

5. Your subconscious mind will believe whatever you repeatedly tell it, and so if you really believe that the money is out there waiting for you to get it, your subconscious mind will believe it too and then it will come.

6. Don't wait for your plan before you start visualizing the money. Visualize first and the plan will come.

7. Write out your affirmation statement and put it where you can see it and read it aloud twice a day. But, don't just read it with a boring, monotone voice. Read it as if you already had the money. Read it with excitement and passion and emotion.

8. Don't worry if it feels strange or you don't believe what you are saying at first. Your subconscious is listening.

9. This is the process by which ideas are transmuted into money.

# Exercises

1.  Close your eyes and visualize yourself having the following amounts of money separately.

**$10,000**
**$50,000**
**$75,000**
**$100,000**
**$250,000**
**$500,000**
**$1,000,000**
**$5,000,000**
**$10,000,000**
**$50,000,000**
**$100,000,000**
**$500,000,000**
**$1,000,000,000**

At which level were you unable to visualize the money? That is your "money ceiling" and in order to be able to manifest more than that, you need to consciously visualize yourself having more money than that.

Please note that every single amount on the list above is already owned by someone somewhere so while you may have a challenge seeing yourself with an amount it is a self imposed challenge that can easily be broken!

2.  In the following space, write an affirmation that you can read aloud several times a day to see and feel yourself already in possession of your goal:

_____

_____

_____

# Chapter 5 — Specialized Knowledge, Personal Experiences or Observations

## Key Ideas

1. You're going to need to develop specialized knowledge in order to become successful. Probably more than you want.

2. If you don't have the specialized knowledge in some area, develop a relationship with someone who does.

3. You can buy knowledge, either through someone who has it or through education.

4. If you're thinking about going back to school, make sure you have a purpose for doing so. What, specifically, do you need to know?

5. Employers will pay more for workers with specialized knowledge.

6. If you're not making the kind of money you want, take a personal inventory and see if you should consider changing careers or going back to school.

7. There is no cure for a lack of ambition.

8. You don't have to start at the bottom and work your way up. It can cause you to get into a rut and lose your ambition.

9. We rise to high positions or remain at the bottom BECAUSE OF CONDITIONS WE CAN CONTROL IF WE DESIRE TO CONTROL THEM.

10. Both success and failure are largely the results of HABIT!

## Exercises

1.  What specialized knowledge can you obtain in order to become more successful? Describe it here:

    _____

    _____

    _____

2.  What benefits will you get if you can get the specialized knowledge you described earlier?

    _____

    _____

    _____

3.  What people/organizations currently have the specialized knowledge you need to be more successful?

    _____

    _____

    _____

4.  How, when and where can you get this specialized knowledge from them?

    _____

    _____

    _____

5.  Who can you develop a relationship with that has some specialized knowledge that you need but don't want or need to get yourself? An example might be an accountant or a financial advisor.

    | Name | Type of Knowledge |
    | --- | --- |
    | _____ | _____ |
    | _____ | _____ |
    | _____ | _____ |

6.  If you don't know anyone, do some research and find someone and/or organizations that have specialized knowledge that would add to your success.

    _____

    _____

    _____

# Chapter 6 — Imagination: the Workshop of the Mind

## Key Ideas

1. A person can create anything that he or she can imagine.

2. The brain is both a broadcasting, and a receiving station for the vibration of thought.

3. There are two forms of imagination: synthetic and creative.

4. Synthetic imagination is that which rearranges old ideas into new ones. It doesn't develop anything new.

5. Creative imagination develops something completely new.

6. If your imagination has dried up you can bring it back by using it.

7. The secret is not a secret. You see it all around you.

8. If someone else has done it, so can you.

9. Often you can get the money quickly if you make a definite decision to do so and a definite plan for how.

10. Hard work and honesty alone do not bring riches. Riches, when they come in huge quantities, are never the result of HARD work alone!

11. Riches come, if they come at all, in response to definite demands, based upon the application of definite principles, and not by chance or luck.

## Exercises

1. Describe a time when you used your synthetic imagination—that is, when you rearranged ideas into a new way.

   _____

   _____

   _____

2. Describe a time when you used your creative imagination—that is, when you developed a completely new idea.

   _____

   _____

   _____

3. State a specific amount of money you currently desire?

   _____

   _____

   _____

4. State the exact date by which you want to have this money?

   _____

   _____

   _____

5. What are your definite demands for the money? What do you need it for?

   _____

   _____

   _____

# Chapter 7 — Organized Planning, the Crystallization of Desire into Action

## Key Ideas

1.  This chapter teaches you how to create a practical plan for changing desire into action.

2.  You need to form a group with other people so that you can access their experience, education, intelligence, and knowledge.

3.  If your first plan doesn't work, make a new one.

4.  You WILL experience temporary defeat. Overcoming the defeat is often the thing that allows you to succeed.

5.  Most great leaders started out as followers.

6.  Here are the important attributes of leaders.

    i.    UNWAVERING COURAGE.
    ii.   SELF-CONTROL.
    iii.  A KEEN SENSE OF JUSTICE.
    iv.   DEFINITENESS OF DECISION.
    v.    DEFINITENESS OF PLANS.
    vi.   THE HABIT OF DOING MORE THAN PAID FOR.
    vii.  A PLEASING PERSONALITY.
    viii. SYMPATHY AND UNDERSTANDING.
    ix.   MASTERY OF DETAIL.
    x.    WILLINGNESS TO ASSUME FULL RESPONSIBILITY.
    xi.   COOPERATION.

7.  Here are the ten major causes of failure in leadership.

    i.    INABILITY TO ORGANIZE DETAILS.
    ii.   UNWILLINGNESS TO RENDER HUMBLE SERVICE.
    iii.  EXPECTATION OF PAY FOR WHAT THEY "KNOW" INSTEAD OF WHAT THEY DO WITH THAT WHICH THEY KNOW.
    iv.   FEAR OF COMPETITION FROM FOLLOWERS.
    v.    LACK OF IMAGINATION.
    vi.   SELFISHNESS.
    vii.  INTEMPERANCE.
    viii. DISLOYALTY.
    ix.   EMPHASIS OF THE "AUTHORITY" OF LEADERSHIP.
    x.    EMPHASIS OF TITLE.

8. The first impression you make is the one that lasts. Pay attention to how you present yourself in your manner of dress, the neatness of your written materials, and in the other ways that you present your image.

9. There are seven steps to getting exactly the position you want.

   i. **First.** Decide EXACTLY what kind of a job you want. If the job doesn't already exist, perhaps you can create it.

   ii. **Second.** Choose the company, or individual for whom you wish to work.

   iii. **Third.** Study your prospective employer, as to policies, personnel, and chances of advancement.

   iv. **Fourth.** By analysis of yourself, your talents and capabilities, figure WHAT YOU CAN OFFER, and plan ways and means of giving advantages, services, developments, ideas that you believe you can successfully deliver.

   v. **Fifth.** Forget about "a job." Forget whether or not there is an opening. Forget the usual routine of "have you got a job for me?" Concentrate on what you can give.

   vi. **Sixth**. Once you have your plan in mind, arrange with an experienced writer to put it on paper in neat form, and in full detail.

   vii. **Seventh.** Present it to the proper person with authority and he will do the rest.

10. The real employer of the future will be the public.

11. The QUALITY and the QUANTITY of service rendered, and the SPIRIT in which it is rendered, determine to a large extent, the price, and the duration of employment.

12. The 30 major causes of failure are:

    1. UNFAVORABLE HEREDITARY BACKGROUND.
    2. LACK OF A WELL-DEFINED PURPOSE IN LIFE.
    3. LACK OF AMBITION TO AIM ABOVE MEDIOCRITY.
    4. INSUFFICIENT EDUCATION.
    5. LACK OF SELF-DISCIPLINE.
    6. ILL HEALTH.
    7. UNFAVORABLE ENVIRONMENTAL INFLUENCES DURING CHILDHOOD.
    8. PROCRASTINATION.
    9. LACK OF PERSISTENCE.
    10. NEGATIVE PERSONALITY.
    11. LACK OF CONTROLLED SEXUAL URGE.
    12. UNCONTROLLED DESIRE FOR "SOMETHING FOR NOTHING."
    13. LACK OF A WELL DEFINED POWER OF DECISION.
    14. ONE OR MORE OF THE SIX BASIC FEARS.
    15. WRONG SELECTION OF A MATE IN MARRIAGE.
    16. OVER-CAUTION.
    17. WRONG SELECTION OF ASSOCIATES IN BUSINESS.

18. SUPERSTITION AND PREJUDICE.
19. WRONG SELECTION OF A VOCATION.
20. LACK OF CONCENTRATION OF EFFORT.
21. THE HABIT OF INDISCRIMINATE SPENDING.
22. LACK OF ENTHUSIASM.
23. INTOLERANCE.
24. INTEMPERANCE.
25. INABILITY TO COOPERATE WITH OTHERS.
26. POSSESSION OF POWER THAT WAS NOT ACQUIRED THROUGH SELF EFFORT.
27. INTENTIONAL DISHONESTY.
28. EGOTISM AND VANITY.
29. GUESSING INSTEAD OF THINKING.
30. LACK OF CAPITAL.
31. UNDER THIS, NAME ANY PARTICULAR CAUSE OF FAILURE FROM WHICH YOU HAVE SUFFERED THAT HAS NOT BEEN INCLUDED IN THE FOREGOING LIST.

# Exercises

1. Which of the following qualities of leaders would you say you have? Which do you need to develop?

   | Quality | Have | Need |
   | --- | --- | --- |
   | Unwavering Courage | | |
   | Self Control | | |
   | Sense of Justice | | |
   | Definiteness of Decision | | |
   | Definiteness of Plans | | |
   | Doing More Than Paid For | | |
   | Pleasing Personality | | |
   | Sympathy and Understanding | | |
   | Mastery of Detail | | |
   | Assuming Full Responsibility | | |
   | Cooperation | | |

2. Pretend you are meeting yourself for the first time. What is the first impression you have?

   _____

   _____

   _____

3. Describe what is good about yourself?

   _____

   _____

4. Describe what is bad about yourself?

   _____

   _____

5. What could you improve to present a better image?

   _____

   _____

6. Describe how "the public" is really your employer:

   _____

   _____

   _____

# SELF-ANALYSIS QUESTIONNAIRE FOR PERSONAL INVENTORY

1. Have I attained the goal which I established as my objective for this year? (You should work with a definite yearly objective to be attained as a part of your major life objective).

   _____

   _____

   _____

2. Have I delivered service of the best possible QUALITY of which I was capable, or could I have improved any part of this service?

   _____

   _____

   _____

3. Have I delivered service in the greatest possible QUANTITY of which I was capable?

   _____

   _____

   _____

4. Has the spirit of my conduct been harmonious, and cooperative at all times?

   _____

   _____

   _____

5. Have I permitted the habit of PROCRASTINATION to decrease my efficiency, and if so, to what extent?

   _____

   _____

   _____

6. Have I improved my PERSONALITY, and if so, in what ways?

   _____

   _____

   _____

7. Have I been PERSISTENT in following my plans through to completion?

_____

_____

_____

8. Have I reached DECISIONS PROMPTLY AND DEFINITELY on all occasions?

_____

_____

_____

9. Have I permitted any one or more of the six basic fears to decrease my efficiency?

_____

_____

_____

10. Have I been either "over-cautious," or "under-cautious?"

_____

_____

_____

11. Has my relationship with my associates in work been pleasant, or unpleasant?

   If it has been unpleasant, has the fault been partly, or wholly mine?

_____

_____

_____

12. Have I dissipated any of my energy through lack of CONCENTRATION of effort?

_____

_____

_____

13. Have I been open minded and tolerant in connection with all subjects?

_____

_____

_____

14. In what way have I improved my ability to render service?

_____

_____

_____

15. Have I been intemperate in any of my habits?

_____

_____

_____

16. Have I expressed, either openly or secretly, any form of EGOTISM?

_____

_____

_____

17. Has my conduct toward my associates been such that it has induced them to RESPECT me?

_____

_____

_____

18. Have my opinions and DECISIONS been based upon guesswork, or accuracy of analysis and THOUGHT?

_____

_____

_____

19. Have I followed the habit of budgeting my time, my expenses, and my income, and have I been conservative in these budgets?

_____

_____

_____

20. How much time have I devoted to UNPROFITABLE effort which I might have used to better advantage?

_____

_____

_____

21. How may I RE-BUDGET my time, and change my habits so I will be more efficient during the coming year?

_____

_____

_____

22. Have I been guilty of any conduct which was not approved by my conscience?

_____

_____

_____

23. In what ways have I rendered MORE SERVICE AND BETTER SERVICE than I was paid to render?

_____

_____

_____

24.  Have I been unfair to anyone, and if so, in what way?

_____

_____

_____

25.  If I had been the purchaser of my own services for the year, would I be satisfied with my purchase?

_____

_____

_____

26.  Am I in the right vocation, and if not, why not?

_____

_____

_____

27.  Has the purchaser of my services been satisfied with the service I have rendered, and if not, why not?

_____

_____

_____

28.  What is my present rating on the fundamental principles of success? (Make this rating fairly, and frankly, and have it checked by someone who is courageous enough to do it accurately).

_____

_____

_____

# Chapter 8 — Decision: the Mastery of Procrastination

## Key Ideas

1. Procrastination is the opposite of decision and is something everyone has to overcome.

2. Every successful person has the habit of making decisions promptly, changing them slowly or not at all.

3. People who fail to accumulate money don't make quick decisions and tend to change them based on the opinions of other people.

4. Every time you open your mouth in front of someone who has a lot of knowledge, you are showing them exactly how much you do and don't know.

5. Genuine wisdom is shown through modesty and silence.

6. Don't tell everyone what you're going to do. Show them.

7. Most people are in the positions they're in (and are earning the income they do) because they failed to make a definite decision to make and execute a plan.

8. You have to make a definite decision rather than let the circumstances of life dictate your position.

## Exercises

1. Describe a time when you procrastinated. What was the result?

   _____

   _____

   _____

2. Describe a time when you were able to make a quick decision. What was different about this?

   _____

   _____

   _____

3. How often do you change your mind?

   _____

   _____

   _____

4. Do you have a tendency to tell everyone what you are going to do instead of showing them? If so, how can you remind yourself not to do this?

   _____

   _____

   _____

# Chapter 9 — Persistence: the Sustained Effort Necessary to Induce Faith

## Key Ideas

1. Persistence and willpower are what transmute desire into money.

2. Most people are willing to throw out their plans at the first sign of resistance. But, in order to attain your goal, you HAVE to be persistent. Everyone experiences setbacks. If you do, change your plan if needed and keep going.

3. The intensity of your desire relates to the intensity of your results. Weak desire leads to weak results. Intense desire leads to strong results.

4. If you're having trouble generating an intense desire and a money consciousness, use your Mastermind Group to help energize you.

5. Unless you are actively engaged in money consciousness, poverty consciousness will take over. Money consciousness is an active state and the default state is poverty consciousness.

6. With persistence comes success.

7. Every failure brings with it the seed of an equivalent advantage.

8. Here are the causes of persistence:

    a. DEFINITENESS OF PURPOSE.
    b. DESIRE.
    c. SELF-RELIANCE.
    d. DEFINITENESS OF PLANS.
    e. ACCURATE KNOWLEDGE.
    f. CO-OPERATION.
    g. WILL-POWER.
    h. HABIT.

9. These are the weaknesses which must be mastered by all who accumulate riches.

    1. Failure to recognize and to clearly define exactly what one wants.
    2. Procrastination, with or without cause. (Usually backed up with a formidable array of alibis and excuses).
    3. Lack of interest in acquiring specialized knowledge.
    4. Indecision, the habit of "passing the buck" on all occasions, instead of facing issues squarely. (Also backed by alibis).
    5. The habit of relying upon alibis instead of creating definite plans for the solution of problems.

6.  Self-satisfaction. There is but little remedy for this affliction, and no hope for those who suffer from it.

7.  Indifference, usually reflected in one's readiness to compromise on all occasions, rather than meet opposition and fight it.

8.  The habit of blaming others for one's mistakes, and accepting unfavorable circumstances as being unavoidable.

9.  WEAKNESS OF DESIRE, due to neglect in the choice of MOTIVES that impel action.

10. Willingness, even eagerness, to quit at the first sign of defeat. (Based upon one or more of the 6 basic fears).

11. Lack of ORGANIZED PLANS, placed in writing where they may be analyzed.

12. The habit of neglecting to move on ideas, or to grasp opportunity when it presents itself.

13. WISHING instead of WILLING.

14. The habit of compromising with POVERTY instead of aiming at riches. General absence of ambition to be, to do, and to own.

15. Searching for all the short-cuts to riches, trying to GET without GIVING a fair equivalent, usually reflected in the habit of gambling, endeavoring to drive "sharp" bargains.

16. FEAR OF CRITICISM, failure to create plans and to put them into action, because of what other people will think, do, or say. This enemy belongs at the head of the list, because it generally exists in one's subconscious mind, where its presence is not recognized.

10. There are four ways to develop persistence.

1.  A DEFINITE PURPOSE BACKED BY BURNING DESIRE FOR ITS FULFILLMENT.

2.  A DEFINITE PLAN, EXPRESSED IN CONTINUOUS ACTION.

3.  A MIND CLOSED TIGHTLY AGAINST ALL NEGATIVE AND DISCOURAGING INFLUENCES, including negative suggestions of relatives, friends and acquaintances.

4.  A FRIENDLY ALLIANCE WITH ONE OR MORE PERSONS WHO WILL ENCOURAGE ONE TO FOLLOW THROUGH WITH BOTH PLAN AND PURPOSE.

# Exercises

1. Describe a time when you had a really intense burning desire for something.

   _____

   _____

   _____

2. What was the result of that intense, burning desire?

   _____

   _____

   _____

3. Describe a time when you only had a moderate desire for something.

   _____

   _____

   _____

4. Were your results less successful than when you had a burning desire for your goal?

   _____

   _____

   _____

5. Describe a time when you gave up on a goal.

   _____

   _____

   _____

6. Why did you give up? Was there something you could have changed so that you would have been able to be persistent?

   _____

   _____

   _____

7. What will you do to stay persistent with your current goal?

   _____

   _____

   _____

# Chapter 10 — Power of the Master Mind: the Driving Force

## Key Ideas

1. There are three sources of knowledge. They are:

   a. INFINITE INTELLIGENCE.
   b. ACCUMULATED EXPERIENCE.
   c. EXPERIMENT AND RESEARCH.

2. No one can gain great power without being a part of a mastermind.

3. There are two elements of a mastermind group. One is economic and the other is psychic.

4. The economic advantage is obvious; when you surround yourself with others who have resources, you have access to them, too.

5. The psychic advantage is more abstract and harder to understand. There is a phenomenon where the energy of a group is bigger and more powerful than that of the individuals within it. This is the power of the mastermind.

6. The positive emotions of thought form can carry one to fortune. The negative emotions of thought form can carry one down to poverty.

7. Poverty and riches often change places.

## Exercises

1.  Are you a part of a Mastermind Group? If so, who is in it? What resources does each person bring?

    _____

    _____

    _____

2.  What benefits have you discovered from your Mastermind Group?

    _____

    _____

    _____

3.  If you're not in a Mastermind Group yet, visit www.RichConsultantClub.com or take the incredible value FREE OFFER on page 72 to experience the benefits of being part of a community of successful Rich Consultants committed to growth and prosperity.

    _____

    _____

    _____

# Chapter 11 — The Mystery of Sex Transmutation

## Key Ideas

1. The word "transmute" means to change one form of energy into another.

2. Sex energy is one of the most powerful creative forces in the world.

3. With willpower, one can transmute sex energy to elevate him or herself to the status of a genius.

4. Scientific research has disclosed these significant facts:

   Fact #1: The men of greatest achievement are men with highly developed sex natures; men who have learned the art of sex transmutation.

   Fact #2: The men who have accumulated great fortunes and achieved outstanding recognition in literature, art, industry, architecture, and the professions, were motivated by the influence of a woman.

5. The emotion of sex contains the secret of creative ability.

6. The mind responds the most to the following stimuli:

   1. The desire for sex expression.
   2. Love.
   3. A burning desire for fame, power, or financial gain, MONEY.
   4. Music.
   5. Friendship between either those of the same sex, or those of the opposite sex.
   6. A Master Mind alliance based upon the harmony of two or more people who ally themselves for spiritual or temporal advancement.
   7. Mutual suffering, such as that experienced by people who are persecuted.
   8. Auto-suggestion.
   9. Fear.
   10. Narcotics and alcohol.

7. The great artists, writers, musicians, and poets become great, because they acquire the habit of relying upon the "still small voice" which speaks from within, through the faculty of creative imagination.

8. Creative imagination is called the "sixth sense."

9. The human mind responds to stimulation! Among the greatest, and most powerful of these stimuli is the urge of sex. When transmuted, this force is capable of lifting people into the higher forms of thought vibration allowing them to think like a genius.

10. The mere possession of this energy is not sufficient to produce a genius. The energy must be transmuted from desire for physical contact, into some other form of desire and action, before it will lift one to the status of a genius.

11. This doesn't mean that one must become a celibate monk in order to use sex energy. The energy of a powerful physical attraction between a man and a woman can be transmuted into desire and action that is expressed in another way than sex. It takes self-discipline to take that energy and use it in another way.

12. Most people don't succeed before the age of 40. This is because the sex energy is so strong that most men have a tendency to focus on sex. After 40, though, the energy dissipates a bit and a person can focus on business success.

13. The vast majority of male success in the world is attributable to sexual chemistry and a man's desire to impress a woman.

14. There are five ways to express personal magnetism, or sex energy. They are:

    1. The hand-shake. The touch of the hand indicates, instantly, the presence of magnetism, or the lack of it.
    2. The tone of voice. Magnetism, or sex energy, is the factor with which the voice may be colored, or made musical and charming.
    3. Posture and carriage of the body. Highly sexed people move briskly, and with grace and ease.
    4. The vibrations of thought. Highly sexed people mix the emotion of sex with their thoughts, or may do so at will, and in that way, may influence those around them.
    5. Body adornment. People who are highly sexed are usually very careful about their personal appearance. They usually select clothing of a style becoming to their personality, physique, complexion, etc.

15. When the emotion of love begins to mix itself with the emotion of sex, the result is calmness of purpose, poise, accuracy of judgment, and balance.

16. One who has loved has never lost.

17. Love, alone, will not bring happiness in marriage, nor will sex alone.

18. When the emotion of romance is added to those of love and sex, the obstructions between the finite mind of man and Infinite Intelligence are removed.

19. Man's greatest motivating force is his desire to please a woman! But most men don't want to admit it.

20. The intelligent woman understands this and doesn't make an issue of it. Some men acknowledge the woman's influence, but many don't.

21. No man is happy or complete without the modifying influence of the right woman.

## Exercises

1.  What are your thoughts on this chapter? Do you agree or disagree with the idea that love and romance and sex are some of the driving forces behind success?

    _____

    _____

    _____

2.  What has been your experience with love, romance, sex, and success? Do you have positive or negative thoughts around it?

    _____

    _____

    _____

3.  Whenever you find yourself thinking a negative thought about love, romance, or sex immediately change it into a positive thought. Stop thinking about the negative experience you may have had in the past and think of a positive one instead.

    _____

    _____

    _____

4.  Describe a time when you felt a physical attraction to someone in the workplace.

    _____

    _____

    _____

5.  How could you have transmuted that energy into passion for your work?

    _____

    _____

    _____

6.  Describe how you could improve your personal magnetism.

    _____

    _____

    _____

# Chapter 12 — The Subconscious Mind: The Connecting Link

## Key Ideas

1. The subconscious mind is the connecting link between the finite mind of man and Infinite Intelligence.

2. The subconscious mind receives and files things you sense and think and it doesn't filter them.

3. You can voluntarily plant things in your subconscious mind.

4. If you don't consciously plant positive things into your subconscious mind, then negative things will get planted by default.

5. The possibilities of creative effort connected with the subconscious mind are stupendous and imponderable.

6. Everything that a person creates begins as a thought.

7. The "mixing" of faith with a plan, or purpose, intended for submission to the subconscious mind, may be done ONLY through the imagination.

8. The subconscious is more sensitive to thoughts that are mixed with feelings.

9. The seven major positive emotions are:

    The emotion of DESIRE
    The emotion of FAITH
    The emotion of LOVE
    The emotion of SEX
    The emotion of ENTHUSIASM
    The emotion of ROMANCE
    The emotion of HOPE

10. The seven major negative emotions are:

    The emotion of FEAR
    The emotion of JEALOUSY
    The emotion of HATRED
    The emotion of REVENGE
    The emotion of GREED
    The emotion of SUPERSTITION
    The emotion of ANGER

11. Positive and negative emotions cannot occupy the mind at the same time. One or the other must dominate. It is your responsibility to make sure that positive emotions constitute the dominating influence of your mind.

## Exercises

1. Which of the seven positive emotions do you engage in on a daily basis?

_____

_____

_____

2. Which of the seven negative emotions to you engage in on a daily basis?

_____

_____

_____

3. In the following spaces, if it is applicable, answer the questions:

I feel fear when I:

_____

_____

_____

I feel jealousy when I:

_____

_____

_____

I feel hatred when I:

_____

_____

_____

I wish I could get revenge when:

_____

_____

_____

I feel greed when I:

_____

_____

_____

I feel superstition when I:

_____

_____

_____

I feel angry when I:

_____

_____

_____

4.  Now in the following spaces, if applicable, answer the question:

    When I am feeling fear, this is what I will do to transmute the fear into faith:

    _____

    _____

    _____

    When I am feeling jealous, this is what I will do to transmute the jealousy into compassion:

    _____

    _____

    _____

    When I am feeling hatred, this is what I will do to transmute the hatred into empathy:

    _____

    _____

    _____

When I desire revenge, this is what I will do to transmute it into peace:

_____

_____

_____

When I am feeling superstitious, this is what I will do to transmute it to logic:

_____

_____

_____

# Chapter 13 — The Brain: A Broadcasting and Receiving Station for Thought

## Key Ideas

1. Every human brain is both a broadcasting and receiving station for the vibration of thought. This means that your brain is sending vibrations as well as receiving it.

2. When the brain is vibrating at a rapid rate, it not only attracts thoughts and ideas released by other brains through the medium of the ether, but it gives to one's own thoughts that "feeling" which is essential before those thoughts will be picked up and acted upon by one's subconscious mind.

3. When one person picks up the thought or a "feeling" that another person is sending out, it's called "telepathy."

4. It is possible to blend different minds together on an energetic plane.

## Exercises

1.  Describe a time when you had a strong sense of what someone else was thinking or doing.

    _____

    _____

    _____

2.  Describe a time when someone picked up on your thoughts.

    _____

    _____

    _____

# Chapter 14 — The Sixth Sense: The Door to the Temple of Wisdom

## Key Ideas

1.  This principle is the apex of the others. You really can't understand it until you've mastered the other twelve.

2.  The sixth sense is what is known as a hunch, a gut feeling, or intuition.

3.  You can only understand the sixth sense by developing from within.

4.  Using the sixth sense is what leads to "miracles."

5.  One way to access the sixth sense is to develop a team of "invisible counselors." These are people you admire and you imagine talking with them about your issues and challenges.

6.  When having the meetings with your invisible counselors, talk to them out loud. This gets your mind more receptive to ideas, thoughts, and knowledge from the sixth sense.

7.  Every deeply seated desire has the effect of causing one to seek outward expression through which that desire may be transmuted into reality.

8.  The ability to use the sixth sense like this takes time and comes after you've applied the principles in this book. It doesn't often come before the age of 40. Usually (if at all) it comes well past 50.

## Exercises

1. How comfortable are you using your sixth sense?

   _____

   _____

   _____

2. Describe a time when you followed your gut, intuition, or a hunch.

   _____

   _____

   _____

3. If you were to create an invisible counseling team, who would be on it? What would be their roles?

Name_____ Role

# Chapter 15 — How to Outwit the Six Ghosts of Fear

## Key Ideas

1.  Indecision becomes doubt which becomes fear.

2.  There are six basic fears. They are:

    The fear of POVERTY
    The fear of CRITICISM
    The fear of ILL HEALTH
    The fear of LOSS OF LOVE OF SOMEONE
    The fear of OLD AGE
    The fear of DEATH

3.  The fear of poverty is a state of mind, nothing else.

4.  The symptoms of the fear of poverty are indifference, indecision, doubt, worry, over-caution, procrastination, and expecting poverty instead of demanding riches.

5.  Criticism plants fear in the mind.

6.  The symptoms of the fear of criticism are self-consciousness, lack of poise, indecisive personality, inferiority complex, extravagance, lack of initiative, lack of ambition.

7.  Fear of ill health is related to the fear of old age and the fear of death.

8.  People can be made ill by suggestion. "You look terrible!"

9.  The symptoms of the fear of ill health are negative autosuggestion, hypochondria, avoidance of exercise, susceptibility, self-coddling, intemperance.

10. The fear of the loss of love is the most painful of al the six basic fears.

11. Women are more susceptible to the fear of the loss of love than men.

12. The symptoms of the fear of the loss of love are jealousy, fault finding, and gambling.

13. The fear of old age is related to a fear of poverty. It's also related to a fear of ill health and the fear of death.

14. The symptoms of the fear of old age are the tendency to slow down, calling one's self "old," dressing too youthful.

15. The fear of death is because no one really knows what happens after we die.

16. If you believe that energy is neither created nor destroyed, then the fear of death is wiped out because nothing ever dies.

17. The main symptom of the fear of death is thinking about dying.

18. The way to overcome any of these fears is to decide to not be afraid of them.

19. You may control your own mind, you have the power to feed it whatever thought impulses you choose. With this privilege goes also the responsibility of using it constructively.

20. The seventh basic evil is the susceptibility to negative influences.

21. To protect yourself from this, use willpower and set up habits that counteract each fear.

22. There are some self-analysis test questions you can ask yourself to see yourself as you really are. They are included, with spaces to write your answers, in this workbook.

23. You have to know your own "alibis" or personal excuses. You defend them because you create them.

24. You are in possession of the Master Key that unlocks the door to Life's bountiful riches. The Master Key is intangible, but it is powerful! It is the privilege of creating, in your own mind, a BURNING DESIRE for a definite form of riches. There is no penalty for the use of the Key, but there is a price you must pay if you do not use it. The price is FAILURE. There is a reward of stupendous proportions if you put the Key to use.

## Exercises

# SELF-ANALYSIS TEST QUESTIONS

1. Do you complain often of "feeling bad," and if so, what is the cause?

_____

_____

_____

2. Do you find fault with other people at the slightest provocation?

_____

_____

_____

3. Do you frequently make mistakes in your work, and if so, why?

_____

_____

_____

4. Are you sarcastic and offensive in your conversation?

_____

_____

_____

5. Do you deliberately avoid the association of anyone, and if so, why?

_____

_____

_____

6. Do you suffer frequently with indigestion? If so, what is the cause?

_____

_____

_____

7. Does life seem futile and the future hopeless to you? If so, why?

_____

_____

_____

8.   Do you like your occupation? If not, why?

_____

_____

_____

9.   Do you often feel self-pity, and if so why?

_____

_____

_____

10.  Are you envious of those who excel you?

_____

_____

_____

11.  To which do you devote most time, thinking of SUCCESS, or of FAILURE?

_____

_____

_____

12.  Are you gaining or losing self-confidence as you grow older?

_____

_____

_____

13.  Do you learn something of value from all mistakes?

_____

_____

_____

14.  Are you permitting some relative or acquaintance to worry you? If so, why?

_____

_____

_____

15. Are you sometimes "in the clouds" and at other times in the depths of despondency?

_____

_____

_____

16. Who has the most inspiring influence upon you? What is the cause?

_____

_____

_____

17. Do you tolerate negative or discouraging influences which you can avoid?

_____

_____

_____

18. Are you careless of your personal appearance? If so, when and why?

_____

_____

_____

19. Have you learned how to "drown your troubles" by being too busy to be annoyed by them?

_____

_____

_____

20. Would you call yourself a "spineless weakling" if you permitted others to do your thinking for you?

_____

_____

_____

21. Do you neglect internal bathing until auto-intoxication makes you ill-tempered and irritable?

_____

_____

_____

22. How many preventable disturbances annoy you, and why do you tolerate them?

_____

_____

_____

23. Do you resort to liquor, narcotics, or cigarettes to "quiet your nerves"? If so, why do you not try willpower instead?

_____

_____

_____

24. Does anyone "nag" you, and if so, for what reason?

_____

_____

_____

25. Do you have a DEFINITE MAJOR PURPOSE, and if so, what is it, and what plan have you for achieving it?

_____

_____

_____

26. Do you suffer from any of the Six Basic Fears? If so, which ones?

_____

_____

_____

27. Have you a method by which you can shield yourself against the negative influence of others?

_____

_____

_____

28. Do you make deliberate use of auto-suggestion to make your mind positive?

_____

_____

_____

29. Which do you value most, your material possessions, or your privilege of controlling your own thoughts?

_____

_____

_____

30. Are you easily influenced by others, against your own judgment?

_____

_____

_____

31. Has today added anything of value to your stock of knowledge or state of mind?

_____

_____

_____

32. Do you face squarely the circumstances which make you unhappy, or sidestep the responsibility?

_____

_____

_____

33. Do you analyze all mistakes and failures and try to profit by them or, do you take the attitude that this is not your duty?

_____

_____

_____

34. Can you name three of your most damaging weaknesses?

_____

_____

_____

35. What are you doing to correct them?

_____

_____

_____

36. Do you encourage other people to bring their worries to you for sympathy?

_____

_____

_____

37. Do you choose, from your daily experiences, lessons or influences which aid in your personal advancement?

_____

_____

_____

38. Does your presence have a negative influence on other people as a rule?

_____

_____

_____

39. What habits of other people annoy you most?

_____

_____

_____

40. Do you form your own opinions or permit yourself to be influenced by other people?

_____

_____

_____

41. Have you learned how to create a mental state of mind with which you can shield yourself against all discouraging influences?

_____

_____

_____

42. Does your occupation inspire you with faith and hope?

_____

_____

_____

43. Are you conscious of possessing spiritual forces of sufficient power to enable you to keep your mind free from all forms of FEAR?

_____

_____

_____

44. Does your religion help you to keep your own mind positive?

_____

_____

_____

45. Do you feel it your duty to share other people's worries? If so, why?

_____

_____

_____

46. If you believe that "birds of a feather flock together" what have you learned about yourself by studying the friends whom you attract?

_____

_____

_____

47. What connection, if any, do you see between the people with whom you associate most closely, and any unhappiness you may experience?

_____

_____

_____

48. Could it be possible that some person whom you consider to be a friend is, in reality, your worst enemy, because of his negative influence on your mind?

_____

_____

_____

49. By what rules do you judge who is helpful and who is damaging to you?

_____

_____

_____

50.  Are your intimate associates mentally superior or inferior to you?

_____

_____

_____

51.  How much time out of every 24 hours do you devote to:

    a.    your occupation

    b.    sleep

    c.    play and relaxation

    d.    acquiring useful knowledge

    e.    plain waste

52.  Who among your acquaintances,

    a.    encourages you most

    b.    cautions you most

    c.    discourages you most

    d.    helps you most in other ways

53.  What is your greatest worry? Why do you tolerate it?

_____

_____

_____

54.  When others offer you free, unsolicited advice, do you accept it without question, or analyze their motive?

_____

_____

_____

55.  What, above all else, do you most DESIRE? Do you intend to acquire it?

_____

_____

_____

56. Are you willing to subordinate all other desires for this one?

_____

_____

_____

57. How much time daily do you devote to acquiring it?

_____

_____

_____

58. Do you change your mind often? If so, why?

_____

_____

_____

59. Do you usually finish everything you begin?

_____

_____

_____

60. Are you easily impressed by other people's business or professional titles, college degrees, or wealth?

_____

_____

_____

61. Are you easily influenced by what other people think or say of you?

_____

_____

_____

62. Do you cater to people because of their social or financial status?

_____

_____

_____

63. Whom do you believe to be the greatest person living?

_____

_____

_____

64. In what respect is this person superior to you?

_____

_____

_____

65. How much time have you devoted to studying and answering these questions? (At least one day is necessary for the analysis and the answering of the entire list.)

_____

_____

_____

# Chapter 16 — Creating Your Rich Consultant Personalized Action Plan

This chapter is where you bring all the progress you have made in the workbook together and create your personalized Rich Consultant Action plan.

If you have completed all the questions honestly, congratulations! You should now have an increased sense of self-awareness that most people never have. You have also demonstrated a good sense of commitment to tasks you start; we now know that perseverance is a basic requirement of the "Think & Grow Rich" mindset.

There are two simple parts to getting rich as a Consultant, the first is learning what to do and the second is doing it until you succeed. A major problem most Consultants face is definitely not in the knowing *what to do,* its mostly in *doing it* and *more importantly doing it the profitable way!*

You must be totally committed to doing more with your life and learning more about yourself. Make sure you regularly study successful people and interact with them as often as you can. This is extremely important as it will give you realistic benchmarks to compare yourself with while providing you with ideal role models and mentors to aspire to.

This section challenges you to do some deep self-analysis in order to get increased clarity on the best way to achieve the success you desire. It introduces you to the specially developed Rich Consultant Success Framework®, this is a unique methodology designed by Consultants for Consultants to clarify the best route to riches.

This is the most important part of this workbook as it is where you develop your own personalized Rich Consultant Action plan. Your plan will be a very valuable resource to you as it will help to clarify the best way forward and detail what exactly you need to be doing to become a Rich Consultant.

If you need any extra help completing this section you should attend the free tele-seminar at www. RichConsultantWorkbook.com/Teleseminar as it will guide you through the process.

# The Rich Consultant Framework ®

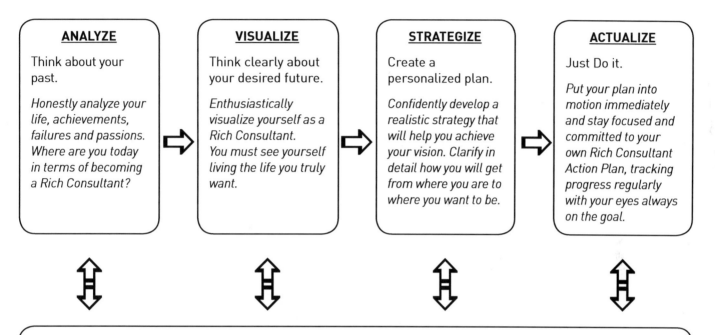

The Rich Consultant Framework® is a conceptual tool specially developed to help consultants achieve financial success. It consists of four sequential processes that provide the individual components of a personalized success plan. The four processes are ANALYZE; VISUALIZE; STRATEGIZE and ACTUALIZE and these processes must be based on a firm foundation of FLEXIBILITY and FEEDBACK.

The Rich Consultant Framework® is detailed in the diagram and this section takes you through the process of using the framework to develop your own unique and personalized Rich Consultant Action Plan®.

1. Analyze

   Review your life to date, what have you done. Identify your achievements, challenges and failures. This is where you explore what you have done with your life and where it had brought you. Identify what has worked for you in the past and why. What hasn't worked for you and why.

   _____

   _____

   _____

   _____

   _____

   _____

   _____

   _____

   _____

   _____

   _____

   _____

   _____

   _____

   _____

   _____

   _____

   _____

   _____

   _____

   _____

   _____

   _____

   _____

2.  Visualize

    Visualize your ideal future as a Rich Consultant and describe this in detail. What are you doing? How do you do it? Describe your typical day? What is your specialization and how are you monetizing your knowledge skills and experience. How much do you charge and how do you interact with your clients.

    This is your chance to create the Rich Consultant lifestyle in your mind, your opportunity to really *"Think and Grow Rich"!*

    _____

    _____

    _____

    _____

    _____

    _____

    _____

    _____

    _____

    _____

    _____

    _____

    _____

    _____

    _____

    _____

    _____

    _____

    _____

    _____

3. Strategize

You now have a detailed understanding of where you currently are and a clear description of where you are going. Now you need to create a realistic, achievable plan of what exactly you have to do to get you there. Who do you need to become to attract the level of success you want?

Do you need to get extra training, get a mentor, get a new job or resign from your current job? What are the sacrifices you must make to create the new you? Do you need new friends and/or new business partners? Do you need to join a Mastermind or a community of like-minded Consultants?

Prepare a detailed list of everything you need to do to achieve the success you deserve. You must put a date beside each task indicating when you must get it done as this creates your personal deadlines for each stage of your growth.

_____

_____

_____

_____

_____

_____

_____

_____

_____

_____

_____

_____

_____

_____

_____

_____

_____

_____

_____

_____

4. Actualize

This is the easy and exciting stage because you have to *JUST DO IT!* Plans are great tools but they are useless if not implemented. You cannot make an omelet without breaking some eggs. You also cannot create the new Rich Consultant you will become without changing the current you.

Move boldly into your future and do whatever is required to create the successful future you require. You may want to start with the smaller tasks and progress gradually to the bigger tasks.

_____

_____

_____

_____

_____

_____

_____

_____

_____

_____

_____

_____

_____

_____

_____

_____

_____

_____

_____

_____

5. Flexibility & Feedback

Your Rich Consultant Action Plan® must be built on a strong foundation of Flexibility and Feedback. If one plan doesn't work out exactly as you planned you must be flexible enough to change and try a different approach until you do succeed.

Always be vigilant for feedback from all your actions; was it good or bad? How was it received? How can it be improved? Feedback will help you with all this as it will help you to adapt your Rich Consultant Action Plan® in line with current realities and market demands.

To become a Rich Consultant you must offer services and products that the market actually wants and is willing to pay for. It's really not about what you think the market needs or wants and Feedback is how you will realize what exactly this is.

Keep a journal of your progress and record all feedback you get from your efforts including successes and setbacks, these will help you to successfully adapt your strategy according to the realities of the market and your environment.

_____

_____

_____

_____

_____

_____

_____

_____

_____

_____

_____

_____

_____

_____

_____

_____

_____

_____

# About Toks K. Oyegunle

Interestingly, many clients, including a number of very successful Consultants, fondly refer to Toks as the "Consultants Consultant" due to the tremendous value they regularly get from his advice, newsletters, speeches and seminars. He has a detailed understanding of the Consultancy business coupled with an uncanny ability to transfer his extensive knowledge and experience while motivating and inspiring people to achieve levels of success they never believed was possible with their life and businesses.

Toks is the founder of the Consultants Academy (www.TheConsultantsAcademy.com), a coaching and training organization dedicated to helping aspiring and existing Consultants acquire the skills, techniques and strategies required to grow their business considerably and increase profit dramatically.

Toks is a consultant, an author and a serial entrepreneur with experience of creating and successfully managing a number of consultancy firms. These include an IT Consultancy Company, a Financial Technology Consultancy/ Software House, and a Technology Recruitment Consultancy. He has been retained to advise Government as a Consultant on IT Policy and has also advised Non Profits on business development and growth strategies. He has 18 years detailed experience covering consultancy, entrepreneurship and technology.

As a published author, he has written a number of books including – Technology Consultants Success Manual: The Path to Wealth for Technology Consultants, Think & Grow Rich: The Consultants and Knowledge Workers edition (a revised and updated version of Napoleon Hill's classic – Think & Grow Rich); Think& Grow Rich Workbook for Consultants and Knowledge Workers and the Rich Consultant Success Secrets: Seven Keys to Wealth, Joy & Fulfillment for Consultants.

He has won a number of awards and prizes including the GAB Entrepreneur of the Year Award and has been featured regularly in the press including the Young Managers list and the Information & Communication Technology Apostles list.

The long journey to the pinnacle of his profession started with getting a degree in Computing Studies, but his inherent passion for business drove him to follow this with a Masters degree in Business Systems Analysis and Design at the City University in London. He is also an alumnus of the prestigious Harvard Business School where he honed his business and entrepreneurship skills with some of the best brains in the world.

He started his career as an Analyst Programmer with a Financial Technology Consultancy firm in the City of London and quickly rose to become a Consultant to many major Investment Banks. He subsequently left to become one of the highest paid IT Consultants in the City at the time with clients including JP Morgan Chase; Credit Suisse, Deutsche Bank amongst many others.

Toks is passionate about teaching people how to monetize their skills, knowledge and experience as a Consultant.

To contact Toks: Toks@TheConsultantsAcademy.com

# SPECIAL BONUS:
# Rich Consultant Success Secrets Book

If you have completed this workbook you should definitely be congratulated! Most people that start with a workbook like this will never finish it due to one reason or the other. More importantly you will have learned that there is a particular mindset that most self-made rich people appear to have. They actually think differently from the masses and therefore their life turns out extremely different than the masses.

You should have developed your own uniquely personalized Rich Consultant Action Plan® with clear vision on what you will be doing to achieve the financial success you desire. This is the foundation of your Rich Consultant career, the steps you will be taking on the path to financial freedom as a Consultant. There is a special bonus available to you to help you on your journey to success. This includes the Rich Consultant Success Secrets eBook and other benefits included in the incredible value offer, but more on this later.

Let's first explore why I love doing this. I am dedicated to helping people who wish to succeed as Consultants achieve the success they desire for a number of reasons; the first is because I believe I have fortunately been blessed to accumulate considerable wealth as a consultant, so it definitely gives me a sense of joy and fulfillment to help others do the same.

The second reason is somewhat more practical, having started my career as a Junior Consultant at a Financial Technology Consultancy company my first job was as a typical Knowledge Worker, I was a programmer responsible for developing software solutions for the business challenges our clients had at the time. Our clients were typically the major Investment Banks and Fund Management firms in the City of London and I still have fond memories of developing trading systems, investment management systems, and credit risk management systems amongst others.

My extensive professional background coupled with my entrepreneurial career makes me the ideal person to teach others what exactly success requires in this industry. What does this mean to you? What are you trying to achieve with all this? This is the starting point for everybody and you must take time to develop your personal life plan detailing where you are going and how you believe you can get there. Simply reading a few books will give you the basic information you need but that is not enough I'm afraid. You need to take massive action to realize your dreams, you need to physically put yourself in close proximity with others who have already achieved what you want to achieve. This experience alone will shorten your learning curve considerably.

This workbook is targeted at existing and aspiring consultants because they are well positioned to "Think & Grow Rich". If you aspire to become a Rich Consultant you need to get some specialist education, skills and experience in the area you wish to become a Consultant. This will typically be as some sort of Knowledge Worker or the other as it is more suitable to Consultancy services.

Once you get the appropriate education you will progress to getting a job as a knowledge worker, this job will really help you to develop your professional skills and experience. This is what you will leverage to become a Consultant and the first part of the journey will be over.

The next challenge is how to create the transformation you will obviously require to progress from an average Consultant to a Rich Consultant. One that has successfully established multiple streams of income, expert status in your industry and an asset base that will ensure you stay a Rich Consultant for the rest of your life.

At the Consultants Academy, all we do is help existing and aspiring Consultants achieve spectacular success and joy in their business. We specialise in providing the training, coaching and educational support that takes our members and students to success levels they previously did not imagine was possible.

I invite you to sample the Consultants Academy for FREE by getting the Rich Consultant Success Secrets eBook in addition to the other valuable offers available. You are actually going to get a lot more than a FREE eBook in the Incredible Value Free Gift Offer. You will get the opportunity to belong to a great community of Rich Consultants from all over the world. You will get access to the monthly newsletter that details success secrets that work. Step by step instructions on what Rich Consultants are doing now to generate considerable fortunes.

To take advantage of this $573.88 success creating package developed specifically for Consultants just complete the Offer Form on page 72 and email it back to us immediately. Alternatively you may also complete the offer form online if you prefer, just go to www.TheConsultantsAcademy.com/WorkbookOffer.

You have NOTHING to lose and EVERYTHING to gain by continuing your journey to financial success with this free offer. I look forward to hearing from you and helping you to move forward on your personal journey to tremendous success as a Rich Consultant!

# The Incredible Value FREE Gift Offer!

## www.TheConsultantsAcademy.com/WorkbookOffer
## $573.88 of Success Generating Information for Consultants

I really want to test drive the Incredible Value FREE Gift Offer from the Consultants Academy and receive a steady stream of Rich Consultant success generating information which includes:

- **E-Book: The Rich Consultant Success Secrets – Seven Keys to Wealth, Joy and Fulfillment for Consultants (Value = $49.97)**
- **Gold Rich Consultant Inner Circle Coaching (Two Month Value = $199.94)**
  - *Two Issues of The Rich Consultant Monthly Newsletter*
  - *Two CD's of The Exclusive Gold Audio Monthly Interview*
  - *Rich Consultant Gold Member RESTRICTED ACCESS WEBSITE*
  - *At least 25% discount on Future Rich Consultant Events & Seminars*
  - *Book Club & Book Recommendations*
  - *Online Consultant Marketing Strategies (Priceless!)*
- **The New Member Rich Consultant Income Growth Guide (Value = $29.97)**
- **The New Member Income Growth Teleseminar (Value = $97.00)**
- **Rich Consultant Success Webinar (Value = $197.00)**

There is a one-time charge of $19.95 in North America or $39.95 International to cover postage for 2 issues of the FREE Gold Membership. You will automatically continue at the lowest Gold Member price of $99.97 per month ($129.97 outside North America). Should you decide to cancel your membership you may do so at anytime by sending an email to the Consultants Academy at orders@TheConsultantsAcademy.com. Remember, your credit card WILL NOT be charged the low monthly membership fee until the beginning of the 3rd month, which means you will receive 2 full issues to read, test and profit from all of the powerful techniques and strategies you get from being a Rich Consultant Inner Circle Gold Member. And of course it's impossible for you to lose, because if you don't LOVE everything you get, you can simply cancel your membership after the second free issue and never get billed a penny for membership.

---------------------------------------------------------------------------------------------------------------------

## *EMAIL REQUIRED TO NOTIFY YOU ABOUT THE INCOME GROWTH TELESEMINAR AND THE RICH CONSULTANT SUCCESS WEBINAR.*

Name _____ Business Name _____

Address_____

City_____ State_____ Zip_____ Country_____

Email _____

Phone _____ Fax _____

Credit Card: _____Visa _____MasterCard _____American Express _____Discover

Credit Card Number _____Exp. Date _____

Signature _____ Date_____

Providing this information constitutes your permission to Consultants Academy to contact you regarding related information via mail, e-mail, fax and phone

EMAIL COMPLETED FORM TO: orders@TheConsultantsAcademy.com

OR

COMPLETE THE FORM ONLINE AT: www.TheConsultantsAcademy.com/WorkbookOffer

Made in the USA
Lexington, KY
12 March 2017